30 Days to Align Your Health & Healing

30 DAYS TO ALIGN YOUR HEALTH & HEALING

LATOYA STAFFORD

TABLE OF CONTENTS

INTRODUCTION

As a child, I always found comfort in food. Whenever I would have a bad day at school, was sad about something, or just did not feel well, I would use food to make me feel better. When I was growing up, I could have anything I wanted to eat. I had constant access to cakes, cookies, pies, and everything else in between that made you feel good on the inside. Healthy eating was not the primary goal in my household. Most of the food came from a package with little to no nutrients.

No one specifically monitored how much I ate but as I began to grow and develop at a rate much faster than other girls my age, my family pointed out to me I needed to back away from the table and be conscious of my eating habits. At the age of 8 years old, I would make attempts to stick my finger down my throat after eating to avoid gaining weight. After a few attempts, I realized that forcing myself to vomit caused too much pain. I made the conscious decision to not eat in front of certain family members who would express concerns about my weight.

In my teenage years, although I had blossomed into a full-figured girl, I was very active at my age. I participated in recreational activities at school, had a job, and hung out with friends. Still facing my early childhood struggles from being overweight, I thought I was doing something good by being active. I felt good about myself when I was enjoying those activities; even though my internal battle of low self-esteem constantly made me doubt my outer appearance. Kids would make fun of me for being overweight or they would ask uncomfortable questions about my body. I could not make the correlation as to why I was not losing weight with my active lifestyle and I was exhausted from trying to figure it out. My relationship with food further spiraled out of control as I could not control my emotional eating.

Now, as an adult, I remained on a constant quest to fix my body, fix my weight, and fix me. The relentless teasing and lack of family support took a toll on my mental state. I struggled with food addiction, yo-yo dieting, and body dysmorphia. When I was growing up, food was not used as a tool to nourish the body, but was used as a survival mechanism. I did not eat healthy and that trait followed me into adulthood as most of my meals consisted of carbs, a starch, and something sweet, with a soda to drink. I was constantly feeding my body toxic foods that kept me in a cycle of sugar cravings and binge eating. The more I participated in this addictive cycle of eating low nutritional value foods, my health, self-esteem, self-worth, and professional opportunities were impacted by my poor decisions. I knew I was tired of living this way, but I did not know how to break these unhealthy, repetitive patterns over my life.

After losing an unexpected pregnancy at twenty weeks, I experienced severe hormonal changes which included a six-month menstrual cycle. I was later diagnosed with polycystic ovarian syndrome better known as PCOS. At that point, I became proactive about taking control of my health and changing my lifestyle. I felt I finally had an answer for the unexplained stubborn weight loss, but I still struggled with overcoming other physical and mental health impairments that were making my life complicated.

It became a challenge to complete activities of daily living, making successful decisions, and doing things that I once enjoyed such as socializing with friends and leaving the house. Doctors provided me with no solutions to the PCOS diagnosis and I was led to believe that I would spend the rest of my life involuntarily participating in medical experiments until the doctors better identified how to provide relief to women who suffered from PCOS.

At the time of my diagnosis, I was a young, aspiring professional and a newlywed. I knew I wanted to someday start a family. I was told I would never become a mom and had lost my only shot with the miscarriage. I was told I would become diabetic, and that other conditions would develop while living with PCOS. Determined to defeat the odds, I began my journey to live a natural and holistic lifestyle. I have since become a mother of two, while successfully managing my symptoms to live a fulfilled life.

30 Days to Align Your Health and Healing is my invitation for you to gain insight on my personal journey of how I aligned my health and healing. My goal is for you to become self-aware in areas of your life that need healing. I hope to encourage and inspire your own journey of healing as you align your mind, body, and soul.

HOW TO USE THIS JOURNAL:

At the beginning of each section, I share my personal struggles as it relates to mental and physical health, and how I relied on my relationship with God to restore balance and harmony in my life.

This journal is designed to help you explore your mind, body, and soul and to identify deficiencies that prevent you from living a fulfilled life. After reading my personal message, you will be provided with ten journaling days in each section to help facilitate your self-healing journey. My goal is for this journal to help you become a better advocate for yourself in areas of the mind, body, and spirit.

Please note: This journal is not intended to treat, diagnose, or replace any medical advice you have received. Continue to consult with your medical professional regarding your mental and/or physical health. You are welcome to use this journal to write down any notes to share with your doctor, to document your emotional health, to recite positive affirmations, and to list your overall health and wellness goals.

Please refer to this journal often, especially when you feel the need to refocus and realign your passion with your purpose.

THE MIND

The purpose of our brain is to store collected information and then process that information to tell our bodies how to react and respond. Most of how we conduct our day-to-day lives is based on information collected during our childhood. This information is collected through our family, environment, and behaviors we've seen modeled from people of influence.

But what does the brain have to do with our wellness journey? The brain is the home of our central nervous system. When our central nervous system is presented with trauma, repetitive disappointments, and lack of nutrients, the chemistry in our brain is altered. This affects the natural order of how the brain is designed to work.

When the brain experiences a chemical imbalance caused by trauma, it can lead to the part of the brain that controls thoughts, emotions, and feelings being suppressed. To feel good, we manipulate the brain to create a sense of adequacy, and when that feeling disappears, the addictive cycle repeats itself seeking the pleasure and reward we desire.

So how do we fix this? **By recognizing our mental state is in need of healing.** It took me twenty years to realize I needed mental healing from unresolved emotional trauma in my childhood and adult years. I have lived with anxiety for as long as I can remember. And when I started my healing journey, I recognized it was important for me to know when I experienced that first feeling of uncertainty.

I recalled my first thought of anxiety with losing all my grandparents within a short time frame at a young age. When my grandmother died, my parents talked with me and my sisters and explained that we would not be seeing our grandmother again. When I entered my grandparents' house, realization set in that she was no longer here. I was filled with so much unexplainable emotion. But at that young age, I did not know how to process or communicate those emotions. I felt like I had to be there for my family as everyone grieved this life that meant so much to so many people.

By the age of ten, I had lost all of my grandparents except one. As a child, I hated when someone died. I could not cope with the cycle of grief. Therefore, I found ways to suppress that feeling of sadness, like avoiding funerals in my adulthood. However, I enjoyed the food at repasts. In the south, the repast is where the celebration of life begins, where good memories of our loved ones are shared, and there is always an abundance of food and good times had all around.

As an adult, I faced other traumatic events that led to more issues with unprocessed emotions, and I continued to abuse food to feel better. When I felt bad about overeating, I would attempt to diet or restrict my eating to feel good about myself again. But the thought of dieting was short lived as soon as I started feeling better. Then I'd experience an emotional distress that I could not handle, and I would binge eat to deal with my emotions so I could gain clarity.

Years of unmanaged anxiety developed into obsessive thoughts and compulsive eating. When I could not eat, I did other compulsive acts like shopping and obsessive thinking of unhealthy thoughts. I avoided crowds due to heightened sensitivity, and I would replay the events leading up to the death of a loved one wondering what I could have done differently that might result in them still being alive with me today. No matter the situation, I was constantly lost in my thoughts thinking, *what could I have done differently? Should I have spoken up more, done more, did something differently?* It was always a battle, living out of my head instead of living in the now.

When I decided to seek professional help to identify the source of my anxiety, I realized that my anxiety was due to the loss of my routine, the lack of control I had over certain things and certain situations and most importantly, the loss of control I had over my emotions. Routine makes people feel safe and secure and it gives you something to control. When my grandmother passed, my entire life was altered. Visiting her on a regular basis, having meals with her, and spending the night with her was no longer a part of the daily routine. We went to her house often, and in her absence, I felt disconnected. My grandmother was one of my protectors and my security blanket. I also struggled with how to express my feelings about her death. I did not really know how then, but I have since learned that grief is a part of the life cycle. That process of life must be talked about in order to understand it. I have also learned that it is okay to show vulnerability. Everything is not perfect, and neither am I but expressing myself and my feelings reduces emotional distress.

Anxiety is classified as a feeling of tension and uncontrollable thoughts. It is a crippling disorder that can take over your life and eventually tears down your body. If you are unable to control your anxiety, please seek professional assistance with taking back control of your life.

To continue working on your path to becoming a self-healer, take a moment to explore ways that you can heal your mind.

DAY 1

AFFIRM

"Today will be a good day. I will not allow stress and negative thoughts to control my mind. Today is a new day and a new beginning. I will be successful at everything I do today."

List other affirmations that you can begin your day with to help manifest the type of day that you deserve.

DAY 2

AFFIRM

"I am grateful for my life and the people that are in it. Every person in my life has a purpose and although I may not be aware of their purpose, I am grateful to have positive people in my life that are a learning vessel to support my journey of greatness."

Write a letter of gratitude to your support system. Journal ways that you are thankful for them and ways that you will continue to appreciate them for their role in your life.

THE MIND

DAY 3

AFFIRM

"I love myself. I commit to love myself every day because love is the greatest gift I can give myself."

Write a letter of appreciation to yourself. On this day, you can also take yourself on a date. Cook a nourishing meal that will enhance your positivity. Over dinner, recite your appreciation letter to yourself. Frame this letter as an appreciation gift to yourself.

DAY 4

AFFIRM

"Fear serves no purpose in my life."

Repeat this affirmation as many times as needed throughout the day. Journal your fears and ways that you can overcome them.

THE MIND

DAY 5

AFFIRM

"Goodness will follow me through all the days of my life."

Today, do something good for yourself and for someone else. Describe how this made you feel. Is this something you would like to continue? Journal why this is important to you.

THE MIND

DAY 6

—∼∼—

AFFIRM

"Healthy food provides nourishment to my body and I feel good when I eat well."

Plan to eat food that provides nutritional value to your body today. Journal how the food made you feel and the nutritional value each food served to the body's purpose on this day. Journal ways you can continue to eat nutritional value foods on this journey.

DAY 7

―⌁―

AFFIRM

*"I am strong and I can do this. I will not make excuses
to quit or give up. I will accomplish all my goals."*

Journal about a time when you wanted to quit but
you did not. Describe how you felt when the task was
accomplished. What emotions did you feel?

THE MIND

DAY 8

———— ❧ ————

AFFIRM

"I will allow myself the opportunity to grow. Lifestyle changes can be hard and doing something new can be intimidating. I will not be afraid to take this new risk in loving and bettering myself."

Journal ways that you can grow into this lifestyle. Document the lifestyle changes you are willing to make over the next thirty days.

THE MIND

DAY 9

AFFIRM

"What I put into this journey is what I will get out of this journey. My hard work will pay off in the long run."

Write a letter of forgiveness to yourself. Journal ways that you have learned from those experiences.

THE MIND

DAY 10

AFFIRM

"I will have a healthy mind, body, and spirit."

List five things you will do to ensure that you will have a healthy mind, body, and spirit.

THE MIND

PERSONAL TIPS TO
MANAGE ANXIETY

Declutter living spaces. Find ways to manage and limit impulsive shopping. Only buy things that are essential and necessary. Every few months, reassess your living spaces and declutter as necessary.

Accept the things that you cannot change and learn to live more in the moment.

Practice cognitive behavior therapy by changing patterns and ways that you do things. For example, not visiting some of the restaurants where you might binge eat.

Practice mindfulness and meditate. There are several free apps available to use to play meditation music and/or assist you with guided meditation. This is a great practice in the morning or before you go to bed.

Eat foods that are nutrient conscious. This involves eating a more whole foods diet that reduces and eliminates caffeine and processed foods.

HEALING ACTIONS
FOR THE MIND

REFLECT

Identify your trauma.

_____

_____

_____

_____

How did you react to this trauma?

_____

_____

_____

_____

Have you sought help with this trauma?

_____

_____

_____

_____

EXPLORE

- Who in your family shares this trauma with you? Who have you told about this trauma?
- How did your family member(s) resolve their trauma?
- Is your family supportive of you healing this trauma?

ACTIVITY

- Locate a resource (i.e., therapy, self-help books and online support groups) to help you cope with this trauma.
- Identify ways to help when you are triggered by this trauma.
- Create a sacred space so you can journal, meditate, or relax and release.

THE MIND

THE BODY

The purpose of the body is to house the skeletal system and to allow us the opportunity to perform our tasks for daily living. Our body does this by downloading information from the mind. For women, the body serves an additional purpose as our body represents our femininity, sexuality, and displays our body confidence. After years of toxic and addictive behaviors related to food and other unhealthy lifestyle choices, my physical appearance became unrecognizable. As an adult woman, I felt unattractive and had low self-esteem. Because plus size women clothes were too expensive at the time, to look presentable, I opted to wear men's clothing as an affordable option. Wearing men's clothing affected my mood, personality, my confidence and my attitude.

Men's clothing gave me the option to suppress my emotions and character. Moreover, the psychological effect of all this constructed poor self-image which developed into an unhealthy relationship with my body. This lack of feminine confidence flowed into my professional life. I felt unqualified to compete in the workforce or apply for advancement opportunities because I lacked the confidence to do so.

I thought by losing weight, I would gain the validation I needed to increase my self-worth. After losing eighty pounds through dieting, I remained unhappy with my accomplishment as I still was of large size. I felt as if I looked like a fraud and that I was misrepresenting my brand. As an advocate for a healthy lifestyle and holistic wellness, I was still overweight. I felt I was not qualified to share my experience because I did not "look healthy." This is what the imposter syndrome does. It causes you to doubt your talent, skills, and accomplishments by living in fear of being exposed as a fraud.

One of my exercises in therapy was remembering a situation that made me hate my body. This took me to a time in third grade when I was the only girl with breasts. Girls who were not yet developed teased me relentlessly, and I attempted to make myself less revealing by wearing oversized shirts and sports bras to not get teased. In the fourth grade, my menstrual cycle started, and I had an accident at school. The kids picked at me for days on end about that incident and whenever I would wear my purse to school. I hated being a girl at that age. I was forced to learn and understand my body in ways that were not yet taught to me. Due to the constant teasing at school about being overweight or about feminine issues, I disconnected from my femininity and the bond of female sisterhood.

While working with my therapist, I continued to work on issues as it related to childhood trauma and being bullied as a child about my weight. I had to learn that losing weight did not make you happy about your current body. I needed to be happy with myself with my current weight, and I needed to understand that any weight loss obtained was not an indication of a lifestyle journey. Because I lacked the confidence to illustrate my competence in educating others on how they could thrive with a natural lifestyle, I did a lot of self-care exercises to restore my relationship with my body.

I have had to learn not to compare my journey to others, as each of us has unique bodies. I had to stop being ashamed of my body because I was not at an ideal weight. I had to stop waiting to wear a cute outfit or bright colors or certain articles of clothing because "big girls" were not supposed to wear that. I had to learn how to love myself in my natural form. I may never lose the weight, and that is okay. What I have learned is, this is my body. This is my physical home, and I must appreciate my body in the now and be proud to be a woman. My healing journey is now focused on bettering my health and improving my self-image and self-esteem.

Continue working on your path to becoming a self-healer by exploring ways that you can heal your body.

DAY 1

———✧———

AFFIRM

I appreciate my body as it was made just for me.

Write a letter of appreciation to your current body. Focus on all the positive things about your body and list ways that you are appreciative to your body.

DAY 2

———∼∼∼———

AFFIRM

I love my body. Negativity will not reside in my body.
Only positive energy will flow through my body and
hate will not live inside of me.

When you were writing your letter of appreciation to
your body, did you have any negative thoughts?
Write down each negative thought beginning with, I
love my...

THE BODY

DAY 3

AFFIRM

*I love and admire my body. No one can make me feel
bad about my body.*

When did you first begin to feel negative about your
body? Who made you feel that way?

THE BODY

DAY 4

AFFIRM

I love myself just the way that I am.

How can you be kind to yourself when negative self-talk about your body presents itself?

DAY 5

———⚬⚬———

AFFIRM

I appreciate my body as my body can do anything regardless of its size.

What will you do differently when you feel bad about your body?

THE BODY

DAY 6

———∾∾∾———

AFFIRM

I have a wonderful body. My body will do great things
for me.

Name three ways you can enhance the love for your
body that does not involve losing weight.

THE BODY

DAY 7

———ᔐ———

AFFIRM

Self-care is well-care. I will practice self-care to maintain my wellness relationship with my body.

List a self-care strategy that will help you maintain a positive relationship with your body.

DAY 8

AFFIRM

Food is important fuel to my body.
I will not abuse food on this journey.

How can you be more loving to yourself?

THE BODY

DAY 9

AFFIRM

I trust, love, and respect my body. No one will take that away from me.

Write down ten compliments about your body to yourself.

THE BODY

DAY 10

AFFIRM

"My body is my temple. I will treat my body with love, kindness, and grace. I will not harm my body or allow anyone to make me feel less than regarding my body. I love myself; I accept myself, and I am loving my life freely to be me."

Write down other affirmations for your body that you will recite in the morning before beginning your day.

PERSONAL TIPS
FOR BODY
POSITIVITY

—⁓—

Begin each day with a positive affirmation regarding the body. Affirm: "I love my body, and I will be good to my body today."

If you suffer with poor body image, buy clothing that will make you feel good. Avoid listening to fashion advice. Within reason, if you like it, wear it. Brighten up your wardrobe with color. This is a great way to boost your mood and show your personality.

Exercise for mobility and not to lose weight. Focus on moving your body because you want to be healthier, not skinnier. Enjoy a calming walk or whatever activity you choose, make it fun and enjoyable.

Avoid comparing yourself to others. Comparison is the thief of joy. Appreciate your body and what your body can do for you. Do not discredit the small beginnings on your body positivity journey. Focus on how your body performs and increasing ways to boost your body's performance.

If your body issue becomes overwhelming, consider speaking with a therapist. It is important to focus on healing the childhood trauma that taught you to hate your body. Remember to be kind to yourself during this time.

HEALING ACTIONS
FOR THE BODY

―― ∾ ――

REFLECT

At what age were you happiest about your body?
Why?

_____

_____

_____

_____

Who is your body positivity role model? Why?

_____

_____

_____

_____

What changes do you desire to make to your body? Why?

_____

_____

_____

_____

EXPLORE

- Research different natural body products that will enhance your living experience with your body.
- Explore ways that self-care can improve your relationship with your body.
- Identify ways to remain consistent with your relationship with your body.

ACTIVITY

- Identify clothing that you own that make you proud of your body.
- Discover something new that will help you feel good about your body.
- Locate an accountability partner or service

that can help you on this leg of the journey.

THE SOUL

The purpose of the soul is to connect our character and personality — our inner self and outer self, our physical body and spiritual body. The importance of the soul on your holistic journey is to facilitate the ultimate healing of the mind and body. When you cleanse your soul, this will help adjust the scales of harmony and balance.

When I first decided to recommit to my relationship with Christ, it was very confusing for me. I did not know how to coexist with the person I once was or the people I once called friends. I went through a period of questioning my existence, isolating myself from family and friends, healing my traumas, and ultimately creating the person I wanted to be.

During my healing journey, I relied on my faith to keep my mind focused, to allow my body to not fail me, and to keep a positive attitude on the days I wanted to give up. There were a lot of moments where I had to do self-evaluations to gain a better understanding of my life's path.

I was judged because my spiritual journey did not look like most. I did not attend a church regularly nor could I quote bible scriptures. I wanted to establish a spiritual journey that allowed me to be authentic to myself and my healing. In the end, I learned that I had to establish new boundaries with family and friends such as keeping my relationship between me and God personal and not disclosing ways I practiced my spirituality. I did this so I could strengthen my confidence in Christ in my own way. I learned there is no right way to practice spirituality. I know I am a believer in Christ, and I know I believe in the supernatural healings of God. I should not be made to feel less than because my Christ walk is different from most.

The journey of the soul is different for everyone. We should not be judged based on our acts of faith. For some, practicing gratitude and giving thanks will suffice, and for others, connecting to a higher power is just as meaningful. This is an intimate experience that you can cultivate with the help of this journal. It is important to not feel guilty in this section of the journal. Discover your personal relationship with Christ and continue to Love Life Naturally.

To continue working on your path to becoming a self-healer, take a moment to explore ways you can heal your soul.

DAY 1

AFFIRM

But God commendeth his love toward us, in that, while we were yet sinners, Christ died for us. Romans 5:8

Do you love your life right now? Detail what you love or do not love about your life?

DAY 2

Beloved, let us love one another: for love is God; and everyone one that loveth is born of God, and knoweth God.

Based on what you love or not love about your life, how do you plan on creating the life you want for yourself?

119

DAY 3

AFFIRM

O Satisfy us early with thy mercy; that we may rejoice and be glad all our days. Psalms 90:14

Today, write down what satisfies you?

DAY 4

AFFIRM

But there is a spirit in man: and the inspiration of the Almighty giveth them understanding. Job 32:8

Today, journal about what inspires you?

DAY 5

AFFIRM

God is a Spirit: and they that worship him must worship him in spirit and truth. John 4:24

Do you believe in a higher power? If yes, journal the principles and beliefs of your higher power. If no, do you have any principles and beliefs that you personally live by?

THE SOUL

DAY 6

―――∾―――

AFFIRM

*We are the spirit of God: he that knoweth God heareth
us: he that is not of God heareth not us. Hereby know
we the spirit of truth, and the spirit of error.* 1 John 4:6

Do you have a relationship with a higher power? If no,
would you like a spiritual relationship with a higher
power? Describe your relationship that you have or
the relationship you want to have.

THE SOUL

DAY 7

AFFIRM

And be not conformed to this world: but be ye transformed by the renewing of your mind, that ye may prove what is that good, and acceptable, and prefect, will of God. Romans 12:2

What do you love about your spiritual relationship?

THE SOUL

DAY 8

AFFIRM

Trust in the Lord with all thine heart; and lean not unto thine own understanding. Proverbs 3:5

Would you change anything about your spiritual relationship?

THE SOUL

DAY 9

AFFIRM

*Fulfil ye my joy, that ye be likeminded, having the
same love, being of one accord of one mind.*
Philippians 2:2

Are you fulfilled with your spiritual relationship?

DAY 10

AFFIRM

"My life has a purpose and I will manifest my heart's desires. I am healthy, wealthy, and my life overflows with abundance because greatness never stops."

Continue to journal ways that you can strengthen your spiritual relationship at this time.

PERSONAL TIPS
FOR THE SOUL

Practice gratitude at the start of each day. Give thanks for being blessed with a new day with new opportunities.

Seek spiritual guidance and keep an open mind during your spiritual transformation. Define your spirituality and practice ways you can build your spiritual relationship.

Always practice the golden rule. "Do unto others as you would have them do unto you." This means, if you show love, you will get love. God has extended his grace to all of us. We all are trying to seek our life's purpose and live out our life's purpose. It is important to be kind to each other while we navigate life's journey.

Ask for forgiveness for yourself and for others. We are not perfect, and we are not designed to be perfect. Mistakes are how we learn and grow. Continue to be kind to yourself and others as you transform on your journey.

As our days end, it is important to practice gratitude at the end of each day as well. Give thanks and blessings for the opportunities created and discovered during the day and remember to show God love in all your endeavors.

HEALING ACTIONS
FOR THE SOUL

———— ∿ ————

REFLECT

At what age were you introduced to a relationship with a higher power?

_____

_____

_____

_____

What changes do you desire to make with your current relationship to your higher power?

_____

_____

_____

_____

Will you continue to build upon your relationship with a higher power?

_____

_____

_____

_____

EXPLORE

- Define the purpose of your life.
- Are you living your life's purpose?
- Explore ways that you can connect to your life's purpose.

ACTIVITY

- Continue to use your sacred space for

meditation and healing during this time.

- Locate ways that you can give back to your community by volunteering and community service.
- Attend your place of worship or engage in other activities of worship at least once a month. Use that time to continue strengthening your relationship with your higher power.

ABOUT LATOYA

Latoya Stafford is a wife, mom, and advocate of loving your life in its natural state. After being diagnosed with PCOS, Latoya founded Love Life Naturally to promote a natural and alternative lifestyle that involves focusing on responsible nutrition and loving a life in its natural manner. This meant reducing chemical and toxic load in all areas of life that included food, health, and beauty. Latoya found it imperative to take the necessary measures to heal her mind, body, and spiritual relationship as she could not serve her purpose of servicing others while living with disease.

As Latoya's health evolved, it was important to advocate and bring awareness to how the food we eat affects our mental health, particularly in the areas of food addiction and negative body image. In a world where it can be difficult to get your voice heard regarding issues of health, Love Life Naturally is an advocacy and awareness program that provides you with the confidence to advocate for your life. You can be encouraged to explore holistic options to help you realign your body's divine order.

Be Well and Love Life

Made in the USA
Middletown, DE
02 October 2021

49218935R00096